If You Hold a Seed

by Elly MacKay

SCHOLASTIC INC.

To my mother,

who finds magic in the smallest of places.

To my father,

who showed me the potential of a tiny seed. . . .

ISBN 978-0-545-66172-0

12 11 10 9 8 7 6 5 4 3 2 1 13 14 15 16 17 18/0

Printed in the U.S.A. 40

First Scholastic printing, October 2013

Designed by Frances J. Soo Ping Chow

Edited by Marlo Scrimizzi

Typography: Matchbook, Mr. Moustache, and Sans Serif

If you hold a seed,
And make a wish,
And plant it in the ground…

Something magical can happen.

And if there is some sun . . .

And some rain . . .
It will begin to sprout.

And if you wait . . .

And wait . . .

You will see some little buds,
And tender leaves.

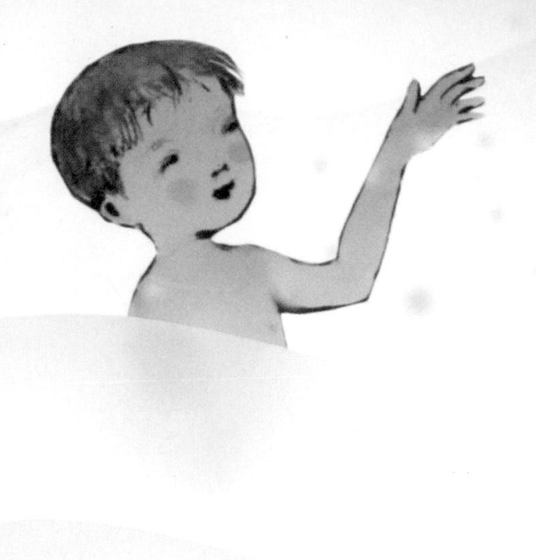

When summer comes,
There might be a bee . . .

...Or perhaps a butterfly.

And they will spread some magic.

But when autumn comes . . .

All its leaves will fall.

Then you will have to wait . . .

Through all the winter days.

Until spring!

The tree will grow,
With buds of gold and green.

Birds will come to perch,
Perhaps to sing.

The tree will soak in the summer sun,
And rain. Then . . .

When autumn comes again,
It will lean into the wind.

And if you wait and wait . . .

Season by season,
Year by year…

That tree will grow SO LARGE
It will hold you.

And . . .

If you wait some more, one day,
Your wish . . .

Will come true.